# Beginner's Guide to Half Marathons: A Simple Step-By-Step Solution to Get You to the Finish Line in 12 Weeks!

by Scott Oscar Morton

© 2017 by LERK Publishing, LLC. All rights reserved.

LERK Publishing, LLC

Edited by Krystal Boots

Cover by LERK Publishing, LLC

ISBN 978-1-947010-02-4

**Follow me on Facebook and Twitter:**

Twitter: @BeginR2FinishR

Facebook: facebook.com/BeginnerToFinisher/

Website: www.halfmarathonforbeginners.com

Email: scottmorton@halfmarathonforbeginners.com

To my kids Luke, Ella, and Ryker.

## Medical Disclaimer

The information in this book is meant to supplement, not replace, proper half marathon training. A sport involving speed, equipment, balance and environmental factors, and running, will involve some inherent risk. The authors and publisher advise readers to take full responsibility for their safety and know their limits. Before practicing the skills described in this book, be sure that your equipment is well maintained, and do not take risks beyond your level of experience, aptitude, training, and comfort level.

# Sign up for FREE EBook releases of my new books at: **http://geni.us/NRtsKu**

## Beginner to Finisher Series:

## <u>**READ FOR FREE**</u> with Kindle Unlimited.

### <u>Available Now</u>

*Why New Runners Fail: 26 Ultimate Tips You Should Know Before You Start Running! Book 1 of 5*

http://geni.us/WhyNewRunnersFail

*5K Fury: 10 Proven Steps to Get You to the Finish Line in 9 weeks or less! Book 2 of 5*

http://geni.us/5kFury

*Beginner's Guide to 10Ks: A Simple Step-By-Step Solution to Get You to the Finish line in 9 Weeks! Book 3 of 5*

http://geni.us/10KTitan

*Beginner's Guide to Half Marathons: A Simple Step-By-Step Solution to Get You to the Finish line in 12 Weeks! Book 4 of 5*

http://geni.us/HM4Beginners

### <u>Coming Soon</u>

*Long Run Motivation*

*Marathon Machine*

# *Table of Contents*

# *Why I Wrote This Book*

I wrote this book for anyone with a burning desire to take their running distance to the next level. I truly want everyone that reads this book to complete a half marathon. If I can help at least one person achieve this goal, then all the time put into this book will be worthwhile.

This book is designed for anyone with a desire to complete a half marathon. If you follow the steps outlined in this book, you will achieve this goal. This book is not intended to be a guide for the experienced runner. Increasing your speed and decreasing your finish times are not covered in this book. Tons of other books and websites cover beating your personal best records and reducing your overall 5k, 10k, half marathon, and marathon run times.

Reasons for running:
- Most races are linked to some worthwhile cause.
- A terrific way to get in shape.
- Great way to feel a sense of accomplishment.

# *Safety*

My goal is for each runner to safely finish a half marathon. Do not attempt to skip the long run sessions, unless you are a seasoned runner or you plan on walking, not running, the half marathon. If you decide to walk the half marathon, make sure that you are in good enough shape to skip the long runs. If you get to race day and you haven't been training according to some long duration training schedule, you could injure your legs, knees, or feet. Running is an impact sport, and your body must get used to running long duration distances. Your legs must be built up to maintain your stamina for the duration of your half marathon race. Building stamina is the sole purpose of having a training cycle that lasts 12 weeks. For marathons, the minimum suggested training cycle is 18 weeks if you have never run a marathon before.

# *Injuries & Medical Conditions*

If you have sports related injuries, I highly suggest that you talk to a medical professional to determine if you are fit enough to endure running a half marathon. Not seeking medical advice could further exacerbate an existing injury. I am not a legal or medical professional, nor am I offering any legal or medical advice. One last time, if you're injured or have medical conditions that prevent you from taking on a rigorous running training program, please seek the opinion of a licensed physician before participating in any physical training. While the training required for a half marathon is not nearly as difficult as the training for a full marathon, it will still push both your mental and physical capabilities.

# *Assumptions*

Before you dive into this book, I'm assuming the following:

- You have a desire to complete your first half marathon.
- You will stick to a training schedule that is provided in this book or elsewhere.
- You can complete a 5k by either walking or running.

If you are having trouble completing a 5k, I have provided three optional weeks on the training schedule. The three optional weeks, labeled A, B, and C, are before the full training schedule. Starting at weeks A, B and C will get you up to speed on completing the distance of a 5k. After completing the distance of a 5k, you will move back into the full 12-week training program.

# Part I - The Runner's Mind

# CHAPTER 1

# *Runner's Mindset*

The runner's mindset. Getting past the fear of running 13.1 miles is one of the biggest hurdles of completing a half marathon. I'm going to let you in on a big secret that helped me get past my fear of having to run 13.1 miles. The secret is that most runners don't run the entire 13.1 miles. Wow, what a secret. It's true. The super athletes and other runners trying to beat their personal best records might very well run the entire race. However, I have completed three half marathons and one full marathon, and the majority of runners will walk through the water/aid stations along the course. Once I realized that you don't have to run the entire distance, the fear of running a half marathon vanished, instantly. My mind had found a chink in the armor. Once I exploited the weakness of the 13.1 half marathon beast, my mindset changed forever on long-distance running. This same technique allowed me to complete a marathon as well. Someone reading this right now is probably saying, "He's probably been running for a long time." I was able to complete three half marathons and one full marathon over the course of a year. I began in May 2016 and completed my third half marathon on April 22, 2017, at the age of 43 with no prior long distance running experience whatsoever. I'm by no means a super athlete, just an average person with high beliefs that I could finish a half marathon. I hope that this encourages you to finish your first half marathon no matter what age you begin at. If I can do it, so can you.

Finishing a 5K or a 10K can be easily accomplished with little or no training at all. If your goal is to run or walk/run a half marathon, then you must tell yourself that you are a runner. You are no longer running for the sake of exercise.

You are running to train your body to complete your first half marathon. You are now training for a half marathon.

Many things that I go over in this book are solely my opinion. Every training schedule discussed within this book has been used by me to complete three half marathons and a full marathon. There are several different schools of thought when it comes to how much running per week it takes to train for a half marathon. There are different nutrition guides, shoe strategies, running miles per week, etc. There is, however, one common thing agreed upon by almost all runners - you have to believe in yourself and believe that you are a runner. Without this firmly ingrained in your head, you won't make it past mile nine, and you won't make it to the finish line. I'm not telling you this to discourage you. I'm telling you this to prepare you for the mental battle of running. One week at a time, one day at a time, one mile at a time, and one step at a time will get you to the half marathon finish line.

# CHAPTER 2

# *The Power of Affirmations*

When I trained for my 5k and 10k races I had no prior knowledge of affirmations. Affirmations are positive action phrases you repeat to yourself on a daily basis to brainwash your mind. I made a list of affirmations that I repeated daily during my half marathon training. Every time before I ran I would tell myself these affirmations:

- I'm a runner.
- I'm training for a half marathon.
- I'm going to complete my half marathon training.
- I'm going to cross the finish line.

After I finished a long run, I would take the affirmations one step further and visualize myself crossing the half marathon finish line.

I contributed most of my success to believing in myself and knowing that failure wasn't an option. By repeating daily affirmations, you can trick your mind into accomplishing almost anything. Affirmations might seem a bit childish. However, they work if you are true to yourself and your level of commitment. Affirmations can be anything that you want them to be, old childhood dreams, new experiences, etc. The power is in the affirmation and hearing yourself say them. Give them a try for a week and see what happens.

The most important running tip is to listen to your body. It's important to know your body and its limitations, especially when you reach the age of forty plus. If your body hurts during a run, slow your pace down or completely stop altogether. Sometimes stopping to stretch for a few minutes will help. During your long training sessions, your mind may begin to fight against your will. When this happens, breathe and repeat some of the affirmations above. Overall, remember that people all over the world finish half marathons all the time. You are no different.

Take a moment and write down a list of at least five affirmations. Title the list "Running Affirmations." Refer to this list every day, especially right before you go on a run.

# CHAPTER 3

# *Failure*

*"I have not failed. I've just found 10,000 ways that won't work."*
- Thomas A. Edison

Failure. Why in the world would I talk about failure? Simple answer, more than likely you will have one bad run if not several bad runs during your training cycle. I had a total of two bad runs on my way to completing my first half marathon. It's important to remember that a failed run is just another step on the path to a successful half marathon finish. During your training sessions if you don't have one lousy run, then consider yourself exceptional. Bad runs occur for many reasons. Here are some possible reasons why a bad run can occur:

- Hungover from the previous night of drinking.
- Didn't get enough sleep because the baby was up every hour crying (The earplugs didn't help at all.)
- Family obligations
- Trying out new foods/gels for your long runs and getting nauseated
- Work obligations
- Self-doubt
- Sick
- Life

Accept the fact that you will more than likely fail at least once during your training cycle. If you completely flop a long run training session, do the following:

- Tell yourself it's OK.

- Readjust your schedule.
- Don't look back.
- Repeat the affirmations you created.

CHAPTER 4

# *Missing a Run*

The one run of the week you don't want to sacrifice is the long run. The long run is the most important run of the week. The day after your long run is just as important so that your body can rebuild your muscles and train your body to store more Glycogen to turn into ATP (adenosine triphosphate). Glycogen will be covered in more depth in the nutrition section of this book. The breakdown and rebuilding of muscles repeatedly happens, building on each week's long run. If you are missing your runs because of a lack of time, try to run in the morning or evening hours. If your work is getting in the way of your training sessions, ask permission to come in late on one of the days of the week. If your work grants permission to come in late one day, try to pick Friday because it will be closer to your actual day of the week that the race will be held. Companies are becoming more flexible with employees' work schedules as long as the work gets done. Some companies take it one step further and sponsor your entry fees into the race. It never hurts to ask.

# CHAPTER 5

# *Motivation*

Why do some people finish marathons and other don't? I believe it comes down to self-motivation and determination. Self-motivation, while probably the strongest of any other form of motivation, is not the only source of motivation. There are several different types of motivation. Three types of motivation that I believe are the most influential come from social media, running partners and yourself.

## Social Media

Social media can help keep you focused and motivated by your circle of friends. You can post running times and screen shots of your runs to social media to let your circle of friends comment and cheer you on. Social media will help perk you up when you have a day that you just don't feel like running.

## Running Partners

Running partners are the next best thing to yourself keeping you motivated. They train with you. They give you feedback. They help you stay on pace. They push you when you have no more energy. Partners also help you stay accountable for following through with your goal. One caveat to a running partner is that if they lack their own source of self-motivation, they aren't going to be of much help motivating you.

## Yourself

Self-motivation is by far the most powerful source of motivation. You know yourself better than anyone else. You are custom to knowing how your mind and body work. If you don't feel like running one day, tell yourself that you will just run a half a mile. After you run a half mile, tell yourself that you will just run one mile. This little trick will help your mind motivate your body to move.

Your motivation could be to get healthy and fit. Also, you could be motivated just to prove to yourself that you can finish a half marathon or to donate to a worthy cause. Whatever the motivation is, you and only you will finish the race.

# *Website*

The running schedules included in this book are available on my website at: www.HalfMarathonForBeginners.com.

## *Action Steps*

- Create your affirmations.
- Determine that you're a runner.

# Part II - Running

CHAPTER 6

# *Selecting Your Race*

Choosing a favorable season as well as selecting a flat course will increase your overall race experience. In Texas, the spring and fall are great times to run. California is an ideal location to train and race due to the year-round fair weather. Many other states are good places to run as well. The California San Jose Rock and Roll Half Marathon race is a relatively flat course.

I made the mistake of picking my first half marathon race without knowing the elevation gain. The race was a small pool of mainly local racers that knew the terrain and course extremely well. The elevation gain will tell you the overall hilliness of the course. The Wurst Race in Muenster, Texas had an elevation gain of nearly 1,000 feet. I'm not kidding. The higher the elevation gain of a course, the more energy you will exert during the race. A course full of hills leads to an overall lower chip time.

For a list of races, please visit the website Running In The USA.

Below is a list of the most common races in the world of running:

| 5k | 3.1 miles | |
|---|---|---|
| 10k | 6.2 miles | |
| 15k | 9.3 miles | |
| 21.1k | 13.1 miles | Half Marathon |
| 42.2k | 26.2 miles | Marathon |
| 50k | 31 miles | Ultra Marathon |

**Table 1**

Anything greater than 26.2 miles is considered an ultra marathon.

# CHAPTER 7

# *Walk, Jog, Run*

Have you ever stopped to consider what speeds are associated with the words walking, jogging, and running? Most people should be able to visualize the different activities. Let's take it one step further and define these activities in technical terms. Associating a rate of speed will help you better define what each of these activities means when I discuss each activity in the rest of the book.

Walking ranges between a speed of 0.1 to 4.0 mph. (Speed walkers walk much faster than this).

Jogging is a tight squeeze between a speed of 4.1 to 6.0 mph.

Running is moving at a speed of more than 6.0 mph.

You can look at these another way. For example, if you travel at a rate of 3 miles per hour, then it will take you 20 minutes to finish 1 mile. The highlighted row in Table 2 shows you the slowest pace you can walk to finish a half marathon within a four-hour cutoff time. In other words, for you to finish a half marathon with a race cutoff time of 4 hours, you have to walk at an average pace of 18.2 minutes per one mile. An easy way to get your mind wrapped around these speeds is to hop on a treadmill. Remember you will have to keep up this average pace for the entire half marathon.

The race cutoff time happens when all water/aid stations are no longer in service. A vehicle of sorts will sweep the course and ask if anyone that hasn't finished the race prefers a lift back to the starting line. You can still finish the race. However, your timing chip might not get to register a finish time. If you don't care about the cutoff time and you just want to finish the race, then your walking pace doesn't matter. Most half marathons will have a cutoff time of 4 hours. I have seen some races with a 3-hour cut-off time. However, you had to pre-qualify in another race with a finish time below 3 hours.

**Tip**

If you can find a race that has both a marathon and a half marathon run on the same day on the same course, you will have a much longer cutoff time (i.e., 7 hours).

Table 2 shows you a predicted finish for a given pace. The slowest pace to finish a half marathon with a cutoff time of four hours is highlighted below in the table (18.2 minutes/mile finishing at 3 hours and 58 minutes).

| Rate/Pace (MPH) | Minutes/Mile | Finish Time (hours) |
|---|---|---|
| 1.0 | 60.0 | 13:06 |
| 1.5 | 40.0 | 8:44 |
| 2.0 | 30.0 | 6:33 |
| 2.5 | 24.0 | 5:14 |
| 3.0 | 20.0 | 4:22 |
| 3.3 | 18.2 | 3:58 |
| 3.5 | 17.1 | 3:45 |
| 4.0 | 15.0 | 3:17 |
| 4.5 | 13.3 | 2:55 |
| 5.0 | 12.0 | 2:37 |
| 5.5 | 10.9 | 2:23 |
| 6.0 | 10.0 | 2:11 |
| 6.5 | 9.2 | 2:01 |
| 7.0 | 8.6 | 1:52 |
| 7.5 | 8.0 | 1:45 |
| 8.0 | 7.5 | 1:38 |
| 8.5 | 7.1 | 1:32 |
| 9.0 | 6.7 | 1:27 |

Table 2

# CHAPTER 8

# *Determining Your Pace*

The simplest way of determining your race pace is to walk a fast-paced mile on a treadmill. Determine what your minutes per mile pace will be. Next, multiply your pace by 13.1, and you will have your overall estimated finish time.

If you've completed a 5k, add about 30 seconds to two minutes to your 5k pace. This will give you a rough estimate of your half marathon predicted pace and total predicted finish time. For example, if you run a 5k at a pace of 10:00 minutes/mile, then your half marathon pace will be somewhere between 10:30 and 12:00 minutes/mile. Using 12:00 minutes/mile as an example, your finish time will be around 2 hours and 37 minutes. You can use Table 3 to see other examples of finish times at different running paces.

The table below shows you a list of predicted half marathon pace times based on your total 5k run time. Remember that these are mere predictions. You could do better or worse depending on how serious you are with your training. The overall average pace for all runners ages 20 - 99 for a 5k is about 10:30 minutes/miles, which is an overall 5k run time of 31:50.

| 5k run time (total) | Half marathon pace (minutes/mile) | Half marathon finish times |
|---|---|---|
| 25:00 | 8:50 | 1:56 |
| 26:00 | 9:10 | 2:00 |
| 27:00 | 9:29 | 2:04 |
| 28:00 | 9:50 | 2:09 |
| 29:00 | 10:10 | 2:13 |
| 30:00 | 10:30 | 2:18 |
| 31:00 | 10:50 | 2:22 |
| 32:00 | 11:15 | 2:27 |
| 33:00 | 11:33 | 2:31 |
| 34:00 | 11:55 | 2:36 |
| 35:00 | 12:15 | 2:40 |
| 36:00 | 12:35 | 2:45 |
| 37:00 | 13:05 | 2:51 |
| 38:00 | 13:15 | 2:54 |
| 39:00 | 13:40 | 2:59 |
| 40:00 | 14:00 | 3:03 |
| 41:00 | 14:22 | 3:08 |
| 42:00 | 14:45 | 3:13 |
| 43:00 | 15:05 | 3:18 |
| 44:00 | 15:30 | 3:23 |
| 45:00 | 15:50 | 3:27 |
| 46:00 | 16:08 | 3:31 |
| 47:00 | 16:30 | 3:36 |
| 48:00 | 16:52 | 3:41 |

| 49:00 | 17:15 | 3:46 |
|-------|-------|------|
| 50:00 | 17:35 | 3:50 |
| 51:00 | 17:55 | 3:55 |
| 52:00 | 18:15 | 3:59 |
| 53:00 | 18:36 | 4:04 |

**Table 3**

# CHAPTER 9

# *Body Posture*

Body tension is your enemy. Most runners don't think of their hand placement during a run. Your arms should sway back and forth naturally without tightening up your fists and pulling them in close to the body. When your body is tense, you are spending extra energy. Try relaxing your shoulders and breathe through a few run cycles. The arms should never reach beyond 90 degrees on the upswing in front of your body.

Your body should be slightly leaned forward with any momentum leaning into the forward traveling motion. Try to keep your head lifted and up. You will be able to run further, allowing your breathing to come and go with ease. If your head is squished into your chest, like you see some runners do, you're not releasing as much carbon dioxide as you should be, causing your breathing to become more difficult. Your breath should be a deep breath in and a deep breath out all the while running anywhere from 10 - 14 steps.

If you notice you have a bounce in your step, you need to have someone record you so that you can watch yourself running. The more bounce in your step, the more impact you will create for the landing foot after takeoff. It's a good idea to watch elite runners in the front of the pack run a race. You will notice that most of their running almost looks like they're gliding. Their feet are extremely close to the ground, and their bodies don't bounce up and down with each stride. If you tend to bounce when you run you are running at a disadvantage, especially during longer runs.

Your body and energy will wear out faster than someone that runs with minimal vertical oscillation (bounce in your step).

# CHAPTER 10

## *Age*

### 30s

After the age of 30, you start losing muscle mass by 1 percent a year. To keep your muscle mass, you need to begin weight resistant training. Not only will weight training help keep your mass, but it will also help burn more calories even when you are sleeping. It's a good idea to try to squeeze in one or two days' worth of weight resistant training as your cross fit exercise. Your leg muscles will become conditioned from all of the long duration running sessions. Let's face it; the weight training will help tone your body and give you a nice upper torso figure to show off on race day.

### 40s

I am a 40s runner. I was fortunate enough to have played sports for many years. I made it to my 40s without sustaining any leg or knee injury. Many of my soccer friends suffered injuries dealing with the ACL, MCL, hamstrings, and meniscus. I believe that my rigorous routine of going to the gym four times a week helped prevent a lot of possible injuries. My routine consisted of 30 minutes of cardio, such as walking, running, or stair master, and 30 to 45 minutes of weight training. I either split my week up into workout routines based on muscle groups— such as Tris and Bis, chest and back, leg and shoulders—or I would work out my entire body on each day and change the exercise for each muscle group for each day.

The 50s, 60s, and 70s

My first half marathon was an interesting race. The overall first place winner was a 13-year-old girl. The overall male master's winner was a 67-year-old man. This man was taller than me and outpaced me by at least two minutes a mile. Don't let the age fool you. I get beat all the time by older people in every race I have ever run. I think it's because veteran runners treat their bodies a lot better than the people in their twenties, thirties, and forties. Also, I believe that the more seasoned a runner, the more easily they can push themselves through the mental battle of running when the running gets difficult.

Just like any age group, your medical condition and fitness will determine your output and performance. No matter what your age is, I recommend consulting with a doctor before running a half marathon and especially if you push on to attempting to complete a marathon.

# CHAPTER 11

## *Rest*

Adequate rest is needed just as much as your actual running hours and miles for training. After your long runs, your body needs time to rebuild and repair the damage taken during your long runs. It takes your legs up to 48 hours after each long run to repair. Your body continues to build your muscles during the rest of the week's runs. Depending on your age, you should be getting an adequate amount of sleep each night. On average the human adult needs anywhere from 7 to 8 hours of sleep. During your training, you need to shoot for getting at least 7 hours of sleep a night. The day after your long runs, you need to take it easy. The first long runs won't be too taxing on your body, but you are creating a habit for your longer runs. If you feel the urge to exercise, I suggest taking a walk for about an hour. Remember, the goal is sustainment of stamina during your race. Your legs need time to repair themselves.

# CHAPTER 12

# *Treadmill Vs. Outdoors*

I began my training running on the old hamster wheel. I soon realized that I could only run up to about 5 miles on a treadmill. I got tired of running in place. Some people can run a long time on a treadmill. I figured out quickly that I'm not that person. If I'm going to run more than 5 miles, I have to have some scenery. I also found that I run a lot faster outside rather than inside by almost an entire minute per mile.

I used the treadmill to run my 5Ks faster. I would use the interval program on the treadmill and run for 60 seconds at a fast pace and then it would automatically shift back to a mild jog pace. The high pace would peak at eight mph, and the slow pace would bottom at five mph. Running intervals allows you to max your VO2 which in turn boosts your long run sustained speed. After an intense interval workout, you will be worn out. These workouts should leave you feeling almost out of breath and fatigued. The good news is you don't have to go near interval training to complete your first half marathon. Interval training for runners is about increasing your running speed as well as maintaining the duration of the pace. Runners who wish to decrease their overall finish time incorporate at least one interval running session per week.

# CHAPTER 13

# *Running*

If you plan on running a half marathon, pat yourself on the back. Running a complete half marathon is no easy feat, but completely doable. I recommend an 8-12 week training schedule depending on what level runner you are. To determine your runner level, figure out how much you currently run per week.

| Miles per week | Weeks needed to train |
|:---:|:---:|
| 0 - 10 | 12 |
| 11 - 20 | 10 |
| 21 - 30+ | 8 |

Runners with 6-10 miles logged per week are probably already running 3-5 miles per session, so their legs are more conditioned to running. However, running 13.1 miles requires your muscles to be trained to run long distances, which requires time, training and rest.

Picking your pace for running comes down to how you feel. If you are out of breath running at a faster pace, then you want to slow your pace down. During your longer runs, I recommend running at a slower pace, anywhere from 1 to 2 minutes per mile slower than you normally would. The key point to the long duration runs is to complete the mileage for the day. Break down your legs and rebuild the muscles and increase the glycogen stores. I ended up finishing faster than my race pace. Race day usually pumps up your excitement and stirs up your adrenalin. Your body will naturally run faster and be more competitive when you are in the midst of a race.

Ways to keep your pace during a race:

1) Smartwatch
2) An app for your phone that allows you to configure how often to shout out your current running pace (i.e., Nike Run Club, Strava, etc.)
3) Find someone else that is running the same pace as you during a race.
4) Have a run buddy that has these devices and keeps the same pace as you.
5) Look for a volunteer pacer team/runner (if the race offers this). Some races have pacers. Running with a pacer lets you concentrate on running and less on the overall time. They will be wearing a specific color shirt or have a band on their arm marking them as a pace leader. Some pacers hold up sticks with a sign showing the total time to complete the race.
6) If you don't care about your pace and you just want to complete a half marathon, then don't worry about it.

# CHAPTER 14

# *Hybrid*

More and more half marathoners are implementing the run/walk method (or hybrid method) for their first half marathon. The run/walk method is useful, especially if you are just beginning your running career at a much later age (i.e., the late 30s, 40s, 50s). The hybrid method involves alternating between walking and running intervals for a specific amount of time. Running should be the heavier of the two. Most half marathon runners will walk through water/aid stations. If you choose to use this method, I recommend you train the same way that you plan on running your race. Some examples below show different forms of run/walk methods. In practice, the easier the method, the easier it is to remember on race day.

1) Run the first 9/10 of a mile and walk the last 1/10 of a mile.
2) Walk the first 1/10 of a mile and run the last 9/10 of a mile. (This starts after the first full mile of running.)
3) Run the first 8/10 of a mile and walk the last 2/10 of a mile.
4) Run 4 minutes, walk 1 minute, run 4 minutes, walk 1 minute. (Jeff Galloway's approach.)
5) Run the first 7.5/10 of a mile and walk the last 2.5/10 of a mile.

These are guidelines; feel free to play with these numbers and find the combination that suits you best. Walking during a race serves multiple purposes. Using walking intervals in between your running intervals can save your legs for the latter part of the race. Secondly, it allows you to conserve some of your energy for the latter part of the race. Last, walking gives you a chance to catch your breath and drink fluids.

# CHAPTER 15

## *Finding Time to Run*

During the twelve-week training period for your half marathon, you will have runs that might last up to three hours. Finding the time to run sometimes takes planning and shifting around your schedules. With family life, kids, wife, dog, other hobbies, etc., anyone's life can get crazily tangled in a gridlock. Your long runs should take place on the weekends or the coinciding day of the week that your race will take place, such as Saturday. Try to run around the same time as your race will take place. Running your long duration runs on the same weekday as your actual race will allow the body to slowly build the habit of waking up and running at the same time.

The time of the day that you choose to run is at your discretion. Some people enjoy running in the morning, and some people enjoy the evening hours.

# CHAPTER 16

## *Weather*

Don't let the weather fool you. Dress for the weather. If it's hot, wear minimal clothes, and when it's cold put on layers.

Wearing as little as possible would probably be best. On long runs, I recommend not running when the temperature is above 80. If you run somewhere where the temperature can reach into the 100s, I recommend running in the morning before the temperature rises above 80 degrees. Every degree above 80 begins to slow down your overall performance during a long run. You can get away with running shorter distances in hotter weather.

When you're training in the cold weather, you need to bundle up. One caveat is once you're warmed up on mile two or three, then you begin to sweat. If you train outside, I would highly suggest that you run a looped route or circuit where you can swing back by and grab any ditched articles of clothing. You can shed clothes and pick them up on the way back. I would purchase inexpensive pullovers or zippered jackets for ease of taking them off during a race. A lot of base layers are being engineered to allow the fabric to breathe, preventing a heat/sweat build up. If you choose to shed layers of clothing during the race, please throw the articles of clothing off the course, not on the course where a runner could trip over it and fall.

Picking the right race at the right time is crucial for running the best race you can slug out. Living in Texas, you don't want to run a half marathon in the middle of the summer. Texas has high humidity levels in the summertime coupled with hot temperatures. Humidity will take the life out of you. It sucks the oxygen out of the red blood cells that are trying to oxygenate your body. In Texas, the fall and spring are the best seasons for running. If you live in the North, your conditions will be more favorable than in Texas. Ideally, you'll want to race when the temperatures are between 50 degrees and 60 degrees.

If you pick a race that is less popular or an inaugural race, you will have a better chance of placing higher in your age group. When you select a more seasoned or crowded race, the competition gets tighter, and you'll place much lower. Also, the best type, of course, is what runners refer to as a flat course. The course is for the most part flat with few hills. Some races will provide the elevation gain, so you'll know how hilly the course will be before racing.

# *Action Steps*

- Pick your race.
- Determine your half marathon pace.
- Set a finish time goal.
- Set a Reach goal.

# Part III - Apparel & Tech Gadgets

# CHAPTER 17

## *Clothes*

Dress for the weather, don't dress for the race. If it's going to be raining, then you probably will want to wear a lightweight poncho. If it's hot, then you will want to dress light. Make sure that you wear a thin layer such as spandex underneath your running shorts to prevent chaffing. Use your common sense when it comes to dressing for your race. When a race is cold, some people will wear "disposable" clothes such as gloves and light jackets that they throw off during the race. They might go back to get them or not. Volunteers will be there to help handle these items that are thrown off. Remember to put your name on items you would like to get back. Some races will have bag checks so that you can place your phone, keys, and other items into your bag that you can pick up at the end of the race.

# CHAPTER 18

## *Shoes*

Selecting the right shoe to run in is one of the most important pieces of a runner's attire. It sounds like a no-brainer, right? Go to your local sports store and buy some "running shoes" that are on sale. Wrong. Good quality running shoes run between $90 and $150+. Mizuno, Brooks, Asics, Adidas, and Nike are probably your best bet. When you buy your shoes through Nike, they give you a 30-day money back guarantee for shoes that you wear and try out. If you test out the shoe and you don't like it for any reason, just return the shoes with free shipping within the 30-day window. Many shoes differ for the different types of runners as well as the different body sizes and shapes. Try out some shoes and find a pair that fits you and doesn't hurt at all.

# CHAPTER 19

## *Socks*

You need to wear proper socks that do not cause blisters. Balega is a great sock that prevents blistering. Other sock brand companies have similar products. Test out other socks and compare. Balega makes high quality, durable socks. Other noteworthy socks are some of the Nike and Under Armour running socks. From my experience, the Balega Ultra Light socks are by far my favorite. Just make sure that you buy 3 to 5 pairs so that you only have to wash socks once a week. The one drawback to Balega is the price. As of this writing, one pair of socks can easily cost $9.99.

# CHAPTER 20

# *Tech Gadgets*

## Smartphone

Some people use their smartphone during all of their runs. It provides both music and running feedback through an assortment of apps that can keep track of your GPS location, pace, run time, distance run, and other key running statistics. Runners that train with phones use a phone case strapped to their upper or lower arms. I have seen other people hold their phone for the length of a race.

## Smart Watch

The smart watch is a great alternative to having to carry a phone. There are numerous choices to look for when purchasing a smart watch.

Most watches cover the basic features listed below:

Common Features:
- Distance ran
- Time Elapsed
- Lapping
- Pace
- Average Pace

Advanced Features:
- Heart Rate
- GPS (without having to carry a GPS-enabled smartphone)
- Timed Interval Walk-Run Notifications

Some of the top smart watches include but are not limited to Apple IWatch 2, Fitbit Surge, and Garmin Vivoactive HR (This is what I wear).

**Heart rate chest strap**

Many sports enthusiasts agree that the chest strap heart rate monitor is the most accurate method of tracking your heart rate. Many people don't want to wear them because you have to attach it across your chest, making them somewhat uncomfortable for long distance races.

# CHAPTER 21

## *Hydration Packs / Water Bottles*

For any run that is longer than six miles or lasts longer than one hour, I wear a hydration pack. Hydration packs allow you to sip and run without stopping. Many people prefer to train with a bottle that has a contoured grip molded into the plastic. Others wear a Hip-Sack that gives you storage for up to three small bottles. Some people don't wear any hydration device, which is perfectly fine due to the abundance of water/aid stations provided on a course. It's all a matter of preference. One thing to consider is any additional packs or water bottles adds to the total weight carried by you. Carrying extra weight increases your drag effect which reduces performance. The winners of most running races are super thin, lean runners. One benefit from training with a hydration pack is the added weight tricks your body into thinking you've packed on a few extra pounds and your body will have to work harder during your training to compensate for the extra weight. If you don't run with your hydration pack at race time, your body will be lighter, and you should run the race faster compared to your training efforts.

Many runners prefer a lightweight handheld running water bottle. Many of the choices now include a zip pouch attached to the water bottle to carry your keys, gels, and even your phone. These are less expensive than a hydration pack, but you have to hold them the entire race unless you are carrying a hip-sack to place them behind your back.

CHAPTER 22

# *Recovery*

A foam roller works wonders for your muscles, especially after your longer runs. These can be purchased for as little as $15.00. I use my foam roller on my legs after any run longer than 6 miles. The foam roller helps move the fascia surrounding your muscles to help release the stiffness that occurs during long-duration runs. Another way to help soothe your muscles is to get a massage. A massage will cost more but could be worthwhile for your legs.

Protein will help your body repair itself after your long duration runs. Make sure that your body is getting enough protein during your 12-week training program.

# *Action Steps*

- Purchase a good pair of running shoes.
- Purchase at least a couple of pairs of running socks.
- Purchase running shirts/tank tops as needed.
- Purchase a sports phone case or smart watch to aid in logging your runs.
- Purchase a sports running bottle or hydration pack for your long runs.
- Purchase a foam roller.
- To prevent chafing wear stretch pants or apply Vaseline on the inner thighs.

# Part IV - Nutrition & Hydration

# CHAPTER 23

# *Nutrition*

Remember that although you will probably be exercising more than you have in your entire life, you still have to keep your food intake in check. I'm not telling you that you have to eat kale leaf sandwiches, etc. Simply try to minimize your sugars, especially from processed food such as sweets. If you drink alcohol, try to avoid drinking every night, or if you do drink don't exceed more than two light beers. The heavy IBU beers easily pack 200+ calories. Some of the breweries in Texas have heavy IBU beers that contain 350+ calories in each 12oz beer. Wow, that's a small snack!

You should treat your weekly long duration runs the same as your half marathon. You will have a total of 12 weeks to train for your first half marathon. Each week will contain a long duration training session which accounts for a total of 12 total runs. These training sessions will prepare you for your 13.1-mile race. From my personal experiences and talking with other runners/cyclists, you have to experiment with your nutrition intake and what you find your body will tolerate. If you have an iron cast stomach and you can eat almost anything, then your choices are endless. When you get closer to race day, you will want to load up more on carbohydrates such as pasta, bread, and brown rice.

For each mile you run, your body will burn roughly 100 calories. 100 calories is an average exertion rate for each mile. People that are larger may burn up to 150 calories per mile run. Your body can absorb roughly 250 calories an hour. Do not over consume calories which could lead to stomach cramping and other ailments.

## chews

1ews and gel packs will give you energy as well as
\ sodium to help you through the race. Some
, such as the Rock -n- Roll Race in Las Vegas, offer
u energy gel packs at their aid stations along the course. Gel
packs and energy chews offer a quick shot of simple
carbohydrates that your body will assimilate almost instantly.
Some runners don't eat anything during a race. Instead, they
just replace their fluids. If this is your first half marathon, then
I highly suggest sticking to the guidelines found at the end of
this book in the weekly schedule. These guidelines will give
you an approximate dosage of the amount of nutrition you
need to help your body finish the race successfully. During a
race, your body will burn anywhere from 500 to 800 calories
per hour depending on your body mass and how efficient
your body is at using energy to run. At the same time, your
body can only absorb between 250 to 300 calories per hour to
replenish your glycogen stores. When you reach mile three,
your body has already burned through the same amount that
you can absorb in one hour. GU Roctane suggests that if you
are going to run for more than 90 minutes, then you need to
eat a gel about 45 minutes into your run. You want to give
your body that extra boost of energy before you're at the
point where you "hit the wall" or "bonk." If you have reached
that point, your body has used up all of its glycogen stores and
energy from the gels/sports drinks. Your body looks for other
sources of energy and begins an assault on your body fat.
Your body takes more energy to burn fat so that energy
exertion makes you even more tired because you are out of
energy and the process to get more energy makes you tired as
well. When your body becomes "insta-hungry" during a long
run, your body is in dire need of calories. You need to eat as
soon as possible.

You can find a half marathon nutrition chart here on the
GU Website. GU Roctane is not the only product available to

consume during your runs. Hammer Gels are also a good alternative. The reason I chose GU was due to the protein and caffeine added to the energy gel. Caffeine can help prevent cramps and give you a boost of energy on top of the energy gel. Most runners that I know as well as cyclists use GU Roctane. I also chew on energy blocks made by Clif. I particularly like the Margarita Clif Shot blocks that have 3x sodium added to each energy shot block.

# CHAPTER 24

## *Glycogen Stores*

Your body uses carbohydrates as its primary source of fuel for races. The primary source of energy for runners comes from glycogen stores. Glycogen is stored primarily in the legs and then secondarily in the liver. The only way to increase the storage of glycogen comes from an ongoing long run training cycle where each long run builds on the next week's long run. Increasing your weekly mileage by about a mile a week will help condition your body for your first half marathon.

Your glycogen stores are where your energy gets pulled from during a race. Your legs followed by your liver and a few other parts of your body hold these important energy stores needed to sustain long duration runs. The glycogen stores first come from what's currently in your stomach and bloodstream. Then it pulls the rest of the glycogen from your legs and liver.

CHAPTER 25

# *Hydration*

Your hydrophilic body needs water which breaks down and dissolves the contents of food. You need to stay properly hydrated for your race. Do not consume too much water. If your stomach is sloshing around liquid before your race, then you have consumed too much water. Try to use the restroom before the race to relieve some of the liquid fullness.

Everyone's body is different, and each person stores water and uses water at different rates. For the most part, drinking about 12 ounces of water before a race and then sipping every 15 minutes before the race should be adequate. You'll have to experiment with your water and nutrition intake during your long training runs. The most important thing to remember is to drink when you are thirsty and drink after eating a gel or snack. Your body needs water to process the food efficiently and to help reduce the possibility of stomach cramps.

There are other techniques outside of the scope of the book to determine your fluid intake requirements for your long runs. One method involves weighing yourself before racing and then drying off after a long run and weighing yourself again. Take note of all of the fluids you consumed before the race and approximate what you drank during your long run. Compare the difference of your pre-run weight with your post-run weight. You will have lost anywhere from .25lbs up to 4.0lbs of body fluids during the long run. Some people sweat much more than others, so this will vary across different body types and body weights. Weather also will affect the loss of body fluids during a race. The hotter the temperature, the more loss of fluids. Important note, make sure you weigh yourself with the same gear/clothes for both re-race weight and post-race weight.

For example, let's look at the following scenario:

| Pre-race weight: | 190.4 |
|---|---|
| Post-race weight: | 187.4 |
| Body fluid loss: | 48oz (3 lbs) |

Fluid intake during the race needs to be right below 48oz.

If you gained weight during a long run (9 miles plus), you need to take extreme caution. Hyponatremia is a severe condition where your body has a lower sodium level than normal. Hyponatremia occurs when you have drunk too much fluid, which in turn, dilutes the sodium levels in your blood. If you are gaining weight during a long duration run, I highly recommend reading up more on Hyponatremia and consulting a doctor. Other symptoms could include nausea, vomiting, headaches, severe cramping, confusion and fatigue.

Most courses will have designated aid stations along the course offering water and sports drinks. Remember to drink when you are thirsty. If you sweat a lot, then you will also want to intake Gatorade or something similar to replace your sodium loss. The sports drink will also have simple sugars to give you more energy to burn. Water is important to drink pre-race, post-race, and during a race. You want to avoid drinking so much water that you can hear the water sloshing around in your stomach. Drinking when you're thirsty will help avoid this problem.

Do not drink alcohol 24-48 hours before your half marathon race. Your body requires 24-48 hours for proper hydration to occur and be absorbed by your cell membranes. Throwing excessive alcohol into the mix will cause inefficient hydration to occur.

# CHAPTER 26

# *Carb Loading*

Carbohydrate loading, or carb-loading for short, is loading your body with carbs. Carb-loading is not a requirement to finish your first half marathon. In fact, you probably don't need to practice this method for a half marathon. Carb-loading plays a much bigger part during your long duration races such as marathons and ultramarathons where you need extra amounts of glycogen coming from your stores to be available for your later miles. Carb loading should be started a week out before the race. Do not carb load the night before your race unless you are sure your stomach can take it. Carb loading does not mean increasing your total caloric intake when compared to your normal training diet. Instead, it means to replace a lot of your fruits and vegetables with servings of high-density carbs.

# *Action Steps*

- Purchase a few hammer gels or GUs online or at a store to see how you can stomach them as fuel for your long runs.
- Start experimenting with your food as fuel for your long runs.
- Log which items seem to give you the best source of energy for your long runs.
- Avoid drinking alcohol the night before your long runs.

# Part V - Training

# CHAPTER 27

## *Set the Training Start Date*

After you select your race date, tell the world about your goal to finish a half marathon on a particular date. Tell your running partner, if you have one, and most importantly tell yourself. Write the goal down. Send yourself an email. Schedule a text message to yourself (you can do this with an Android phone) congratulating you on starting the training program. Once you have determined your race date, you need to work backward to determine when your start date for your half marathon training should begin.

For example, if your race were on November 25th, 2017, then you would count backward 12 weeks which would place your start week on Monday, September 4th, 2017.

| | September | | | | | | |
|---|---|---|---|---|---|---|---|
| Week | m | t | w | t | f | s | s |
| | | | | | 1 | 2 | 3 |
| 1 | 4 | 5 | 6 | 7 | 8 | 9 | 10 |
| 2 | 11 | 12 | 13 | 14 | 15 | 16 | 17 |
| 3 | 18 | 19 | 20 | 21 | 22 | 23 | 24 |
| 4 | 25 | 26 | 27 | 28 | 29 | 30 | |

| | October | | | | | | |
|---|---|---|---|---|---|---|---|
| | m | t | w | t | f | s | s |
| | | | | | | | 1 |
| 5 | 2 | 3 | 4 | 5 | 6 | 7 | 8 |
| 6 | 9 | 10 | 11 | 12 | 13 | 14 | 15 |
| 7 | 16 | 17 | 18 | 19 | 20 | 21 | 22 |
| 8 | 23 | 24 | 25 | 26 | 27 | 28 | 29 |
| | 30 | 31 | | | | | |

| | November | | | | | | |
|---|---|---|---|---|---|---|---|
| | m | t | w | t | f | s | s |
| 9 | | | 1 | 2 | 3 | 4 | 5 |
| 10 | 6 | 7 | 8 | 9 | 10 | 11 | 12 |
| 11 | 13 | 14 | 15 | 16 | 17 | 18 | 19 |
| 12 | 20 | 21 | 22 | 23 | 24 | 25 | 26 |
| | 27 | 28 | 29 | 30 | | | |

# CHAPTER 28

# *Beta Run 13.1*

When I first created my training schedule, I didn't have a beta run 13.1 penciled in. I ended up tweaking my schedule to run past my 12 miles to finish 13.1 miles in a long duration run. Note, completing a beta 13.1 is not required to complete your half marathon training. But I will tell you this, running a beta 13.1 will give you a number that sticks with you before your actual half marathon race. It will tell you at what pace you ran and how long it took you to complete. Completing a half marathon beta run will help you with two things. First, it serves as motivation on race day to beat your beta runtime. Second, it will stamp a sense of accomplishment in your mind knowing that you were able to go the full 13.1 miles regardless of the time it took.

I highly recommend completing at least one 13.1 trial walk/run during your training schedule. Why? It allows you to experiment with your fueling during the race and it takes the pressure and anticipation off of your mind of actually being able to complete a 13.1-mile run. These times don't matter. Here is the result of my 13.1 Beta run.

13.1 Beta
- o Three weeks before half marathon race
- o Total time to complete: 2:28:43
- o 11:21 minutes/mile or 5.3 mph

Actual 13.1 race
- o Total time to complete: 2:11:02
- o 10:01 minutes/miles or 5.9 mph

By setting up two trial runs you can test yourself to see

how fast you will run it and give yourself a goal to try to crush. When I first started out in my training programs, I wrote down three goals to complete my half marathon.

Goal 1 (primary goal): finish by 2:45:00
Goal 2 (reach goal): finish by 2:30:00
Goal 3 (super goal): finish by 2:15:00

I was able to beat my super goal. What you'll find out is that naturally, you will run a faster pace during your actual half marathon race. Your anxiety and nerves will help boost your adrenaline and allow you to run faster than you possibly thought.

# CHAPTER 29

## *Log Sheet*

Logging your runs with an app or on a sheet of paper helps to show the progress you've made. You can compare your early running times with your later running times. Hopefully, you will see somewhat of a gradual increase in performance. I have provided an example of a running log sheet that I created, and it is free to download at Half Marathon For Beginners. Several other websites and apps are available to keep track of this information as well. Keeping a log is not a requirement, but it will help you stay aligned with your goal of completing a half marathon.

There are several apps now available for logging your runs. Garmin Connect and Fitbit automatically log your run based on the device you have connected to your phone. You can keep a simple log sheet on Google Sheets or Microsoft Excel. I would recommend logging the day of the run, the run date, average pace, distance ran, total run time, distance walked, and total walk time.

# CHAPTER 30

## *Cross Training*

There are many different types of exercises that you can do on your cross-training days or even your rest days. If you are tired on your cross training day, then skip the exercises for now. The most important training is your long distance duration training. Walking, bicycling, yoga, kettlebell workouts, and weight training are all great cross-training exercises. A cross training exercise only needs to last between 30 minutes and 1 hour.

# CHAPTER 31

## *Pre-Training Requirements*

Before you begin your 12 weeks half marathon training program, you must be able to walk or run a 5k. The first week of runs is catered to individuals that can complete a 5k distance by either walking or running. If you are having trouble completing a 5k distance, I urge you to allow yourself two to three weeks of additional training. This will extend your total training cycle to 15 weeks. I will refer to these optional training schedules as Week A, Week B, and Week C.

If you are in good enough shape to complete a 5k distance then bypass Week A, B and C. Also, feel free to participate in only two weeks like Week B and C or maybe just Week C. You know your body better than I do, so experiment a little bit to see what best suits your needs.

The summarized running schedules are located after the detailed weekly training schedules.

# CHAPTER 32

# *Cool Downs*

Proper cooling down and stretching is equally important as warming up. I use the following cool down guidelines. These are minimum distances that I walk after my runs. Most of the time I will walk two miles after each run so that I can unwind my legs and stretch.

| Distance Ran | Cooldown (miles) |
|---|---|
| 1-3 | 0.5 |
| 4-6 | 1 |
| 7-9 | 1.25 |
| 10-12 | 1.5 |

## CHAPTER 33

# *Training - Week A (Optional)*

| | |
|---|---|
| Monday | Rest. Take it easy. Don't run. If you need to exercise, I recommend a walk for no longer than 30 minutes. |
| Tuesday | 1 mile (1.5 km) walk/run at an easy pace. If you can easily hold a conversation with someone, then you are running at the right pace. If you're walking, try to maintain a pace no slower than 20 minutes/mile. |
| Wednesday | 1 mile (1.5 km) walk/run at your half marathon pace. Your 5k total time will help predict your half marathon pace. |
| Thursday | 1 mile (1.5 km) walk/run at a medium pace. It doesn't have to be a drastic increase in speed, but try decreasing your half marathon pace by at least 5-10 seconds/mile. So if you walk/run a 12:15 pace, try to run at a 12:05 pace. |
| Friday | Do as little activity as possible. Fridays are important rest days. For your muscles to grow stronger, they need rest. Do not drink alcohol before your long run. |
| Saturday | 1.5 mile (2.5 km) walk/run at a slow pace. The most important piece of your long duration runs is finishing the run. Do not attempt to run these at your half marathon predicted pace. Run at a slower pace than your easy pace. This is typically anywhere from 45 seconds to 2.5 minutes slower than your half marathon predicted pace. |
| Sunday | Rest. For beginner half marathon runners this day needs to be kept at a mild rest day. If your body feels good, then go ahead and do some form of |

| | cross-training for 30 to 60 minutes. |
|---|---|

- Get plenty of sleep the night before your long duration run.
- Try to run your long duration run early in the morning.
- After each of your runs, it's important to stretch out your muscles.

# CHAPTER 34

## *Training - Week B (Optional)*

| Monday | Rest. Take it easy. Don't run. If you need to exercise, I recommend a walk for no longer than 30 minutes. |
|---|---|
| Tuesday | 1.5 mile (2.5 km) walk/run at an easy pace. If you can easily hold a conversation with someone, then you are running at the right pace. If you're walking, try to maintain a pace no slower than 20 minutes/mile. |
| Wednesday | 1.5 mile (2.5 km) walk/run at your half marathon pace. Your 5k total time will help predict your half marathon pace. |
| Thursday | 1.5 mile (2.5 km) walk/run at a medium pace. It doesn't have to be a drastic increase in speed, but try decreasing your half marathon pace by at least 5-10 seconds/mile. So if you walk/run a 12:15 pace, try to run at a 12:05 pace. |
| Friday | Do as little activity as possible. Fridays are important rest days. For your muscles to grow stronger, they need rest. Do not drink alcohol before your long run. |
| Saturday | 2 mile (3 km) walk/run at a slow pace. The most important piece of your long duration runs is finishing the run. Do not attempt to run these at your half marathon predicted pace. Run at a slower pace than your easy pace. This is typically anywhere from 45 seconds to 2.5 minutes slower than your half marathon predicted pace. |
| Sunday | Rest. For beginner half marathon runners this day needs to be kept at a mild rest day. If your body feels good, then go ahead and do some form |

of cross-training for 30 to 60 minutes.

- Get plenty of sleep the night before your long duration run.
- Try to run your long duration run early in the morning.
- After each of your runs, it's important to stretch out your muscles.

# CHAPTER 35

## *Training - Week C (Optional)*

| | |
|---|---|
| Monday | Rest. Take it easy. Don't run. If you need to exercise, I recommend a walk for no longer than 30 minutes. |
| Tuesday | 2 mile (3 km) walk/run at an easy pace. If you can easily hold a conversation with someone, then you are running at the right pace. If you're walking, try to maintain a pace no slower than 20 minutes/mile. |
| Wednesday | 2 mile (3 km) walk/run at your half marathon pace. Your 5k total time will help predict your half marathon pace. |
| Thursday | 2 mile (3 km) walk/run at a medium pace. It doesn't have to be a drastic increase in speed, but try decreasing your half marathon pace by at least 5-10 seconds/mile. So if you walk/run a 12:15 pace, try to run at a 12:05 pace. |
| Friday | Do as little activity as possible. Fridays are important rest days. For your muscles to grow stronger, they need rest. Do not drink alcohol before your long run. |
| Saturday | 3 mile (5 km) walk/run at a slow pace. The most important piece of your long duration runs is finishing the run. Do not attempt to run these at your half marathon predicted pace. Run at a slower pace than your easy pace. This is typically anywhere from 45 seconds to 2.5 minutes slower than your half marathon predicted pace. |
| Sunday | Rest. For beginner half marathon runners this day needs to be kept at a mild rest day. If your body feels good, then go ahead and do some form of cross-training for 30 to 60 minutes. |

- Get plenty of sleep the night before your long duration run.
- Try to run your long duration run early in the morning.
- After each of your runs, it's important to stretch out your muscles.

# CHAPTER 36

# *Training Paces*

Described below are the different paces outlined in the following training schedules that will give you a pace to shoot for during your training runs.

In the first example below, let's assume your 5k overall runtime is at 33:00 minutes which is a pace of 11:00 minutes/mile:

11:33 predicted half marathon pace
2:31:00 predicted half marathon overall finish time

Training Paces will be:

| Slow Pace (Long Run) | 11:33 - 14:03 | 0 to 2 minutes 30 seconds slower than Half marathon pace |
|---|---|---|
| Medium Pace | 11:33 - 12:33 | 0 to 1 minute slower than half marathon pace |
| Half marathon pace | 11:33 | |

In the second example below, let's assume your 5k overall runtime is at 30:00 minutes which is a pace of 10:00 minutes/mile:

10:30 predicted half marathon pace
2:18:00 predicted half marathon overall finish time

Training Paces will be:

| Slow Pace (Long Run) | 10:30 - 13:00 | 0 to 2 minutes 30 seconds slower than Half marathon pace |
|---|---|---|
| Medium Pace | 10:30 - 11:30 | 0 to 1 minute slower than half marathon pace |
| Half marathon pace | 10:30 | |

Remember that these are predictions. My 5k overall run time was at 32:00 which predicted I would finish my first half marathon in 2:27:00. I beat that prediction by almost 16 minutes at 2:11:02. These are simply guidelines to show you how the averages normally pan out.

- After each run, it's important to stretch out your muscles.
- Your long duration runs will begin to become more difficult for week 5 and beyond.
- If you get tired during a long duration run, walk for 1/10 mile or 3-5 minutes.

# CHAPTER 42

# *Training - Week 6*

| Monday | Rest. Take it easy. Don't run. If you need to exercise, I recommend a walk for no longer than 30 minutes. |
|---|---|
| Tuesday | 3 mile (5 km) walk/run at a medium pace. If you can easily hold a conversation with someone, then you are running at the right pace. If you're walking, try to maintain a pace no slower than 20 minutes/mile. |
| Wednesday | 4 mile (6 km) walk/run at your half marathon pace. Your 5k total time will help predict your half marathon pace. |
| Thursday | 3 mile (5 km) walk/run at a medium pace. |
| Friday | Do as little activity as possible. Fridays are important rest days. For your muscles to grow stronger, they need rest. Do not drink alcohol before your long run. |
| Saturday | 8 mile (13 km) walk/run at a slow pace. The most important piece of your long duration runs is finishing the run. Do not attempt to run these at your half marathon predicted pace. Run at a slower pace than your easy pace. This is typically anywhere from 45 seconds to 2.5 minutes slower than your half marathon predicted pace. |
| Sunday | Rest. For beginner half marathon runners this day needs to be kept at a mild rest day. If your body feels good, then go ahead and do some form of cross-training for 30 to 60 minutes. |

- Get plenty of sleep the night before your long duration run.
- Try to run your long duration run early in the morning.
- After each run, it's important to stretch out your muscles.

# CHAPTER 43

# *Training - Week 7*

| | |
|---|---|
| Monday | Rest. Take it easy. Don't run. If you need to exercise, I recommend a walk for no longer than 30 minutes. |
| Tuesday | 3 mile (5 km) walk/run at a medium pace. If you can easily hold a conversation with someone, then you are running at the right pace. If you're walking, try to maintain a pace no slower than 20 minutes/mile. |
| Wednesday | 5 mile (8 km) walk/run at your half marathon pace. Your 5k total time will help predict your half marathon pace. Your training has increased by 1 mile. |
| Thursday | 3 mile (5 km) walk/run at a medium pace. |
| Thursday (optional) | If you plan on running a 10k on Saturday, then lower your run distance to 2 miles instead. |
| Friday | Do as little activity as possible. Fridays are important rest days. For your muscles to grow stronger, they need rest. Do not drink alcohol before your long run. |
| Saturday | 8.5 mile (13.5 km) walk/run at a slow pace. The most important piece of your long duration runs is finishing the run. Do not attempt to run these at your half marathon predicted pace. Run at a slower pace than your easy pace. This is typically anywhere from 45 seconds to 2.5 minutes slower than your half marathon predicted pace. |
| Saturday (optional) | Run a 10k race instead of your long run. This is completely your choice. I recommend running a 10k race. You should see a difference in your race time if you have kept to your training schedule. |

| V | Rest. For beginner half marathon runners this day needs to be kept at a mild rest day. If your body feels good, then go ahead and do some form of cross-training for 30 to 60 minutes. |
|---|---|

- Get plenty of sleep the night before your long duration run.
- Try to run your long duration run early in the morning.
- After each of run, it's important to stretch out your muscles.

# CHAPTER 44

# *Training - Week 8*

| | |
|---|---|
| Monday | Rest. Take it easy. Don't run. If you need to exercise, I recommend a walk for no longer than 30 minutes. |
| Tuesday | 3 mile (5 km) walk/run at a medium pace. If you can easily hold a conversation with someone, then you are running at the right pace. If you're walking, try to maintain a pace no slower than 20 minutes/mile. |
| Wednesday | 5 mile (8 km) walk/run at your half marathon pace. Your 5k total time will help predict your half marathon pace. |
| Thursday | 3 mile (5 km) walk/run at a medium pace. |
| Friday | Do as little activity as possible. Fridays are important rest days. For your muscles to grow stronger, they need rest. Do not drink alcohol before your long run. |
| Saturday | 9 mile (14 km) walk/run at a slow pace. The most important piece of your long duration runs is finishing the run. Do not attempt to run these at your half marathon predicted pace. Run at a slower pace than your easy pace. This is typically anywhere from 45 seconds to 2.5 minutes slower than your half marathon predicted pace. |
| Sunday | Rest. For beginner half marathon runners this day needs to be kept at a mild rest day. If your body feels good, then go ahead and do some form of cross-training for 30 to 60 minutes. |

plenty of sleep the night before your long duration run.

- Try to run your long duration run early in the morning.
- After each run, it's important to stretch out your muscles.

# CHAPTER 45

## *Training - Week 9*

| | |
|---|---|
| Monday | Rest. Take it easy. Don't run. If you need to exercise, I recommend a walk for no longer than 30 minutes. |
| Tuesday | 3 mile (5 km) walk/run at a medium pace. If you can easily hold a conversation with someone, then you are running at the right pace. If you're walking, try to maintain a pace no slower than 20 minutes/mile. |
| Wednesday | 5 mile (8 km) walk/run at your half marathon pace. Your 5k total time will help predict your half marathon pace. |
| Thursday | 3 mile (5 km) walk/run at a medium pace. |
| Thursday (optional) | If you are going to run the 13.1 (21 km) beta run, then do not run today. |
| Friday | Do as little activity as possible. Fridays are important rest days. For your muscles to grow stronger, they need rest. Do not drink alcohol before your long run. |
| Saturday | 10 mile walk/run at a slow pace. The most important piece of your long duration runs is finishing the run. Do not attempt to run these at your half marathon predicted pace. Run at a slower pace than your easy pace. This is typically anywhere from 45 seconds to 2.5 minutes slower than your half marathon predicted pace. |
| Saturday (optional) | I recommend that you attempt to go the full 13.1 miles (21 km) for a half marathon beta run. Only walk/run the first 10 miles (16 km) then walk the last 3.1 miles (5 km). If you are successful, you will have a half marathon ghost time to compete |

| | |
|---|---|
| | against. It will help energize and refocus your training on beating yourself in 3 weeks at the half marathon race. Also, it allows your mind to grasp the achievement of "I have run the distance of a half marathon." |
| Sunday | Rest. For beginner half marathon runners this day needs to be kept at a mild rest day. If your body feels good, then go ahead and do some form of cross-training for 30 to 60 minutes. |

- Get plenty of sleep the night before your long duration run.
- Try to run your long duration run early in the morning.
- After each run, it's important to stretch out your muscles.

# CHAPTER 46

# *Training - Week 10*

| | |
|---|---|
| Monday | Rest. Take it easy. Don't run. If you need to exercise, I recommend a walk for no longer than 30 minutes. |
| Tuesday | 3 mile (5 km)walk/run at a medium. If you can easily hold a conversation with someone, then you are running at the right pace. If you're walking, try to maintain a pace no slower than 20 minutes/mile. |
| Wednesday | 3 mile (8 km) walk/run at your half marathon pace. Your 5k total time will help predict your half marathon pace. |
| Thursday | 3 mile (5 km) walk/run at a medium pace. |
| Friday | Do as little activity as possible. Fridays are important rest days. For your muscles to grow stronger, they need rest. Do not drink alcohol before your long run. |
| Saturday | 11 mile (18 km) walk/run at a slow pace. The most important piece of your long duration runs is finishing the run. Do not attempt to run these at your half marathon predicted pace. Run at a slower pace than your easy pace. |
| Sunday | Rest. For beginner half marathon runners this day needs to be kept at a mild rest day. If your body feels good, then go ahead and do some form of cross-training for 30 to 60 minutes. |

- Get plenty of sleep the night before your long duration run.
- Try to run your long duration run early in the morning.
- After each run, it's important to stretch out your muscles.

# CHAPTER 47

# *Training - Week 11*

| Monday | Rest. Take it easy. Don't run. If you need to exercise, I recommend a walk for no longer than 30 minutes. |
|--------|----------------------------------------------------------------------------------------------------------|
| Tuesday | 3 mile (5 km) walk/run at a medium pace. If you can easily hold a conversation with someone, then you are running at the right pace. If you're walking, try to maintain a pace no slower than 20 minutes/mile. |
| Wednesday | 3 mile (8 km) walk/run at your half marathon pace. Your 5k total time will help predict your half marathon pace. |
| Thursday | 3 mile (5 km) walk/run at a medium pace. |
| Friday | Do as little activity as possible. Fridays are important rest days. For your muscles to grow stronger, they need rest. Do not drink alcohol before your long run. |
| Saturday | 12 mile (20 km) walk/run at a slow pace. The most important piece of your long duration runs is finishing the run. Do not attempt to run these at your half marathon predicted pace. Run at a slower pace than your easy pace. |
| Sunday | Rest. For beginner half marathon runners this day needs to be kept at a mild rest day. If your body feels good, then go ahead and do some form of cross-training for 30 to 60 minutes. |

- Get plenty of sleep the night before your long duration run.
- Try to run your long duration run early in the morning.
- After each run, it's important to stretch out your muscles.

# CHAPTER 48

## *Training - Week 12*

| Monday | Rest. |
|---|---|
| Tuesday | 3 mile (5 km) walk/run at a medium pace. If you can easily hold a conversation with someone, then you are running at the right pace. If you're walking, try to maintain a pace no slower than 20 minutes/mile. |
| Wednesday | 2 mile (1.5 km) walk/run at your half marathon pace. Your 5k total time will help predict your half marathon pace. |
| Thursday | Rest. |
| Friday | Rest. |
| Saturday | Race Day! |
| Sunday | Rest. |

- Get plenty of sleep the night before your long duration run.
- Try to run your long duration run early in the morning.
- After each run, it's important to stretch out your muscles.
- This week your body needs as much rest as possible.
- Don't run past Wednesday.

# CHAPTER 49

# *Training Schedule (Miles)*

This 12 week half marathon training PDF can be downloaded at:

## halfmarathonforbeginners.gr8.com

| Week # | Mon. | Tues. (EP) | Wed. (HMP) | Thur. (MP) | Fri. | Sat. (LD) | Sun. |
|---|---|---|---|---|---|---|---|
| 1 | Rest | 3 mi | 3 mi | 3 mi | Rest | 4 mi | Rest/CT |
| 2 | Rest | 3 mi | 3 mi | 3 mi | Rest | 5 mi | Rest/CT |
| 3 | Rest | 3 mi | 4 mi | 3 mi | Rest | 6 mi | Rest/CT |
| 4 | Rest | 3 mi | 4 mi | 3 mi | Rest | 5k | Rest/CT |
| 5 | Rest | 3 mi | 4 mi | 3 mi | Rest | 7 mi | Rest/CT |
| 6 | Rest | 3 mi | 4 mi | 3 mi | Rest | 8 mi | Rest/CT |
| 7 | Rest | 3 mi | 5 mi | 3 mi | Rest | 10K | Rest/CT |
| 8 | Rest | 3 mi | 5 mi | 3 mi | Rest | 9 mi | Rest/CT |
| 9 | Rest | 3 mi | 5 mi | Rest | Rest | Beta 13.1 | Rest/CT |
| 10 | Rest | 3 mi | 5 mi | 3 mi | Rest | 11 mi | Rest/CT |
| 11 | Rest | 3 mi | 5 mi | 3 mi | Rest | 12 mi | Rest/CT |
| 12 | Rest | 3 mi | 2 mi | Rest | Rest | HM | Rest/CT |

**Table 3**

EP=Easy Pace, HMP=Half Marathon Pace,
MP=Medium Pace,
LD=Long Duration, CT=Cross Train

# Training Schedule (Compact – Miles)

| W | M | T | W | T | F | Sa | S |
|---|---|---|---|---|---|----|---|
| 1 | R | 3 | 3 | 3 | R | 4 | R/CT |
| 2 | R | 3 | 3 | 3 | R | 5 | R/CT |
| 3 | R | 3 | 4 | 3 | R | 6 | R/CT |
| 4 | R | 3 | 4 | 3 | R | 5k | R/CT |
| 5 | R | 3 | 4 | 3 | R | 7 | R/CT |
| 6 | R | 3 | 4 | 3 | R | 8 | R/CT |
| 7 | R | 3 | 5 | 3 | R | 10K | R/CT |
| 8 | R | 3 | 5 | 3 | R | 9 | R/CT |
| 9 | R | 3 | 5 | R | R | B13.1 | R/CT |
| 10 | R | 3 | 5 | 3 | R | 11 | R/CT |
| 11 | R | 3 | 5 | 3 | R | 12 | R/CT |
| 12 | R | 3 | 2 | R | R | HM | R/CT |

Table 4 - Compact Size

# Training Schedule (Beginner - Miles)

| Week # | Mon. | Tues. (EP) | Wed. (HMP) | Thur. (MP) | Fri. | Sat. (LD) | Sun. |
|---|---|---|---|---|---|---|---|
| A | Rest | 1 mi | 1 mi | 1 mi | Rest | 1.5 mi | Rest/CT |
| B | Rest | 1.5 mi | 1.5 mi | 1.5 mi | Rest | 2 mi | Rest/CT |
| C | Rest | 2 mi | 2 mi | 2 mi | Rest | 3 mi | Rest/CT |
| 1 | Rest | 3 mi | 3 mi | 3 mi | Rest | 4 mi | Rest/CT |
| 2 | Rest | 3 mi | 3 mi | 3 mi | Rest | 5 mi | Rest/CT |
| 3 | Rest | 3 mi | 4 mi | 3 mi | Rest | 6 mi | Rest/CT |
| 4 | Rest | 3 mi | 4 mi | 3 mi | Rest | 5k | Rest/CT |
| 5 | Rest | 3 mi | 4 mi | 3 mi | Rest | 7 mi | Rest/CT |
| 6 | Rest | 3 mi | 4 mi | 3 mi | Rest | 8 mi | Rest/CT |
| 7 | Rest | 3 mi | 5 mi | 3 mi | Rest | 10K | Rest/CT |
| 8 | Rest | 3 mi | 5 mi | 3 mi | Rest | 9 mi | Rest/CT |
| 9 | Rest | 3 mi | 5 mi | Rest | Rest | Beta 13.1 | Rest/CT |
| 10 | Rest | 3 mi | 5 mi | 3 mi | Rest | 11 mi | Rest/CT |
| 11 | Rest | 3 mi | 5 mi | 3 mi | Rest | 12 mi | Rest/CT |
| 12 | Rest | 3 mi | 2 mi | Rest | Rest | HM | Rest/CT |

Table 5

EP=Easy Pace, HMP=Half Marathon Pace,
MP=Medium Pace,
LD=Long Duration, CT=Cross Train

# Training Schedule (Beginner Compact Miles)

| | M | T | W | T | F | Sa | S |
|---|---|---|---|---|---|---|---|
| A | R | 1 | 1 | 1 | R | 1.5 | R/CT |
| B | R | 1.5 | 1.5 | 1.5 | R | 2 | R/CT |
| C | R | 2 | 2 | 2 | R | 3 | R/CT |
| 1 | R | 3 | 3 | 3 | R | 4 | R/CT |
| 2 | R | 3 | 3 | 3 | R | 5 | R/CT |
| 3 | R | 3 | 4 | 3 | R | 6 | R/CT |
| 4 | R | 3 | 4 | 3 | R | 5k | R/CT |
| 5 | R | 3 | R | 3 | R | 7 | R/CT |
| 6 | R | 3 | 4 | 3 | R | 8 | R/CT |
| 7 | R | 3 | 5 | 3 | R | 10K | R/CT |
| 8 | R | 3 | 5 | 3 | R | 9 | R/CT |
| 9 | R | 3 | 5 | R | R | B13.1 | R/CT |
| 10 | R | 3 | 5 | 3 | R | 11 | R/CT |
| 11 | R | 3 | 5 | 3 | R | 12 | R/CT |
| 12 | R | 3 | 2 | R | R | HM | R/CT |

Table 6 - Compact Size

# Training Schedule (Kilometers)

| Standard (Kilometers) | | | | | | | |
|---|---|---|---|---|---|---|---|
| Week | Mon | Tue | Wed | Thur | Fri | Sat | Sun |
| 1 | Rest | 5 | 5 | 5 | Rest | 6 | CT/Rest |
| 2 | Rest | 5 | 5 | 5 | Rest | 8 | CT/Rest |
| 3 | Rest | 5 | 6 | 5 | Rest | 10 | CT/Rest |
| 4 | Rest | 5 | 6 | 5 | Rest | 5K Race | CT/Rest |
| 5 | Rest | 5 | 6 | 5 | Rest | 11 | CT/Rest |
| 6 | Rest | 5 | 6 | 5 | Rest | 13 | CT/Rest |
| 7 | Rest | 5 | 8 | 5 | Rest | 10K Race | CT/Rest |
| 8 | Rest | 5 | 8 | 5 | Rest | 14 | CT/Rest |
| 9 | Rest | 5 | 8 | Rest | Rest | 21 Beta | CT/Rest |
| 10 | Rest | 5 | 8 | 5 | Rest | 18 | CT/Rest |
| 11 | Rest | 5 | 8 | 5 | Rest | 20 | CT/Rest |
| 12 | Rest | 5 | 2 | Rest | Rest | Half Marathon | CT/Rest |

CT=Cross Training (30 minutes of biking, walking, yoga, or weight lifting, if you have the energy. If not then simply rest). **21 Beta**=A half marathon test run. Run 16 km and then walk the remaining 5 kms.

# Training Schedule ( Beginner - Kilometers)

| Beginner (Kilometers) | | | | | | |
|---|---|---|---|---|---|---|
| Week | Mon | Tue | Wed | Thur | Fri | Sat | Sun |
| A | Rest | 1.5 | 1.5 | 1.5 | Rest | 2.5 | CT/Rest |
| B | Rest | 2.5 | 2.5 | 2.5 | Rest | 3 | CT/Rest |
| C | Rest | 3 | 3 | 3 | Rest | 5 | CT/Rest |
| 1 | Rest | 5 | 5 | 5 | Rest | 6 | CT/Rest |
| 2 | Rest | 5 | 5 | 5 | Rest | 8 | CT/Rest |
| 3 | Rest | 5 | 6 | 5 | Rest | 10 | CT/Rest |
| 4 | Rest | 5 | 6 | 5 | Rest | 5K Race | CT/Rest |
| 5 | Rest | 5 | 6 | 5 | Rest | 11 | CT/Rest |
| 6 | Rest | 5 | 6 | 5 | Rest | 13 | CT/Rest |
| 7 | Rest | 5 | 8 | 5 | Rest | 10K Race | CT/Rest |
| 8 | Rest | 5 | 8 | 5 | Rest | 14 | CT/Rest |
| 9 | Rest | 5 | 8 | Rest | Rest | 21 Beta | CT/Rest |
| 10 | Rest | 5 | 8 | 5 | Rest | 18 | CT/Rest |
| 11 | Rest | 5 | 8 | 5 | Rest | 20 | CT/Rest |
| 12 | Rest | 5 | 2 | Rest | Rest | Half Marathon | CT/Rest |

**CT**=Cross Training (30 minutes of biking, walking, yoga, or weight lifting, if you have the energy. If not then simply rest).
**21 Beta**=A half marathon test run. Run 16 km and then walk the remaining 5 kms.

# *Action Steps*

- Stick to your training schedule.
- If you can't run on a given day, change your schedule and don't worry about it.
- After your long runs, continue walking for at least 10 minutes or at least 1 mile.
- Cross training will help you stay active on your non-running days.
- A 60-minute walk is an excellent source of cross training.

# Part VI - The Race

# CHAPTER 50

## *Two Days Before the Race*

You will want to eat carbohydrates with every meal. Pasta, rice, and bread are all good sources of carbohydrates to store as glycogen for your race. The week of your race is not the time to overeat. Substitute fruits or vegetables for a serving of carbohydrates. Get plenty of rest. You will gain weight the week leading up to your race. You will lose a bunch of that weight during your run. The night which is two nights before your race is going to be your best chance to get a full night of sleep.

# CHAPTER 51

## *Night Before the Race*

A lot of people will find it difficult to get enough sleep the night before your first half marathon. Some runners will run a few light miles the day before the race. Lay out your running gear so that it will be ready in the morning—just like you have done on each long run training session—which includes your clothing, tech gear, waters, gels, hydration packs, water bottles, running shoes, and socks. If you picked up your running pack for the race early, go ahead and pin the racing number on your shirt or shorts. Do not drink alcohol. If you do drink alcohol, limit yourself to a few drinks. Your body will thank you on race day.

## CHAPTER 52

# *Race Day*

The day has finally arrived. Wake up a couple of hours early before the race start time. (Yeah, I know it's early). Eat a small meal as soon as you wake up. This meal should have some carbohydrates, such as a bagel or toast with peanut butter, maybe a few eggs, and water. Avoid high fiber content food. This meal should be identical to the meals you ate before all of your successful long duration runs. You don't want to change up your routine on race day. I have heard too many stories of people getting sick during a race because they consumed "extra" gels or changed out an energy replacement for something else offered at the race. Stick to your training plan. Drink a cup or two of coffee and drink about 12 oz of water before the race. Continue to sip on water leading up to the race. Remember you don't want a sloshing stomach, so don't over drink. Your body should be hydrated if you began your hydration two days before race day and cut out most alcoholic beverages.

When runners begin to line up for the race, you need to pick the correct starting location in the herd. At most large marathons you will be corralled into finish times to help separate and break up the flow of traffic. If there are no corrals and this is your first half marathon, do not line up at the front of the starting line unless you are going to run the half marathon in 1 hour and 30 minutes. The announcer will state this over and over up until race time. You could easily get stampeded if you attempt to do this or you could hurt someone else. The slowest paced runners such as the walkers need to be in the back of the queue. The average paced runners should be located in the middle of the herd. I have, on many races, thought I was in the correct location somewhere in the middle, and I was wrong. I had to pass many, many people performing slot type racing just to get out of the muck of people. If you are running the race, you need to be in the front of the pack. Roughly between the first 20% and 60% of the racers. The racers at the tail end are planning on walking at a much slower pace. If you need to slow down your pace, then you need to move to the right of the course.

Your blood is pumping, the caffeine is kicking, and the announcer is counting down the last ten seconds before race time. You hear the gun announce the start of the race and you start running way faster than you trained. You reach the 2nd mile still running at an above average training pace time. You reach the third mile, and you have to slow down because you are out of breath from nearly sprinting the last three miles. Now your overall total running time will be much worse than it had been during training. Take it easy out of the gate. Conserve your energy. Steady and even pacing just like your long run training will get you through the race. You will notice that your pace per mile will be faster than your training pace. The excitement, adrenaline and competitive aspects of the race naturally add to the energy surging through your body. So, take it slow at first and run at the pace you've trained at over the last 12 weeks.

# CHAPTER 53

# *Post-Race*

Your body is exhausted, and you might even be a little emotional right now, hanging on to your new, shiny metal, but don't sit down when you cross the finish line. At a bare minimum keep walking for another 10 to 20 minutes. If your body feels good, jog at a light pace for another 10 minutes. Grab something to drink with electrolytes if possible. You need to eat something within at least one hour after your race, to help replenish your body with nutrients and liquids.

If you're up for it, you can drink a beer or two. Drink plenty of water and keep yourself hydrated for the next couple of days. Sometimes a recovery run the day following your race will help stretch out some of your sore leg muscles. Your recovery run should be at a light pace and not last more than thirty minutes.

How long do you have to wait before you start training again? This depends on your age, your body, your recovery time, etc. If your half-marathon was on the way to a full marathon, then you should be ready to start running your next long session within five days. You might need to adjust your other runs for the upcoming week due to the exertion you put forth in the half marathon race. If this is the end of the line for your racing for a while, just take it easy for at least a week. If you get antsy, then go ahead and start running or walking again when your body feels like it. Just remember that your body will be tired for several days after your half marathon. Listen to your body. For example, if you are running 4 miles just 4 days after your half marathon and you start to get winded, that's a sign that your body is still exhausted.

Wait one week before you run more than 3 miles in one running session. Wait two weeks before you run more than 6 miles in one running session. Walking this amount is fine.

For at least seven days after a half marathon, I walk about 4-5 miles a day. I do not run for the first seven days. If I'm in the middle of a marathon training cycle, then I will go ahead and move on to the next long run for the week. If I'm not training for a marathon, then I simply start running again normally about 3-4 miles each day.

# Race Checklist

## Two days before the race:

- You should be tapering now. Don't run.
- Start hydrating - no alcohol.
- Replace some of your food with dense carb food such as pasta and whole grain bread.
- Get at least 7 hours of sleep.

## One day before the race:

- Get all of your gear laid out, including clothes, gels, water, phone, Garmins, and Fitbits.
- Attach your bib number to your clothes.
- Know what route you are going to take to the race.
- Keep hydrating.
- Do not eat a big meal.
- Get at least 7 hours of sleep (might be hard to do this because of anxiety).
- If you are getting edgy, go for a mile or two walk; do not run.

## Race day:

- Wake up at least two hours before your race.
- Eat as soon as you get up. Oatmeal, energy bars, and bananas are great sources of food.
- This meal should be the same as your training session long runs.
- Drink some caffeine 1-2 hours before the race.
- Keep sipping water up until the race.
- Don't consume too much water. If your stomach is sloshing around, you drank too much.

- Arrive at the race a little early if possible just in case of traffic.
- If you plan on taking a gel before the race, take it about 5-15 minutes before the race.

## The Race:

- Don't burst out of the starting line like lightning.
- Race like you trained and you will finish the race.
- Gels taken during the race need to be taken with water for proper assimilation.
- If you are taking energy gels during the race, you won't need to drink sports drinks. Your gels will have enough electrolytes in them.
- Remember you don't have to run the entire race. Slow down to a brisk walk at the water/aid stations for 1/10 mile or 2 minutes then speed back up.

## Post-Race:

- Don't stop moving at the finish line.
- Keep walking for 10 to 20 minutes after the race.
- Grab a sports drink and some food such as a banana, yogurt, or bread.
- Pose for pictures and enjoy your new, shiny medal.
- Stretch your muscles accordingly.
- Don't run for at least 7 days.
- Wait at least 14 days before you run more than 6 miles in one session, unless you are training for a marathon

# Part VII - Troubleshooting

# CHAPTER 54

# *The Wall*

Hitting the wall is when you have no more energy left, and your mind alone can't keep pushing you forward. This typically occurs in runs that last longer than 90 minutes, although technically it could occur at any time, especially over 60 minutes. "Hitting the wall" is nothing more than a complete depletion of glycogen stores and a sudden extreme loss of energy. It is critical, especially since you are a new long distance runner, that you eat before you go on your long runs, typically anything lasting over 90 minutes in duration. You need to pre-fuel for both your half marathon race and your long training runs. During your long runs, you are training your stomach to accept fuel at certain times in the race, just like you are training your legs to run long distances. If you are "hitting the wall" during your long runs, you don't have enough energy. The company GU has a nice chart that shows you how much you are supposed to be eating pre-race and per hour during your races. Fueling is much more important in marathon races because of the duration of the run.

# CHAPTER 55

## *Pains and Tweaks*

Pains that make you want to stop running. These are different than the minor aches and stiffness you get during your run. Many runs I had to stop and just stretch out to alleviate the stiffness. In fact, my muscles aren't fully warmed up until mile number 2. I have yet to have pains that completely stop my running.

As with any physical activity, no two people are exactly alike. The information provided is an example and a guideline, not an absolute rule that you must follow. Adapt anything to your style to suit your needs as a runner. The two best running tips given to me were run naturally and breathe deep. These tips helped me through the long duration runs that can take real effort to complete.

# Part VIII - Conclusion

# *Congratulations*

Pat yourself on the back if you have completed your first half marathon. No matter how long it took you to finish your race, remember that you did something that less than 5% of the United States population has ever done. Congratulations!

# *What's Next?*

If you want to continue your running career, I urge you to either try to beat your personal best half marathon time or move on to marathon training. I took five days off from running then continued my first marathon training. If you have used the training schedules provided in this book, then you should only have to train 6 to 8 more weeks to prepare yourself for a full marathon. I have full faith that if you crossed the half marathon finish line, you can join a tiny percentage of people and add the title of marathon finisher to your life victories.

# *About the Author*

I played sports throughout my youth and even into my adult years. I ran my first 5k at the age of 37 in March of 2008 without any training at all. I finished third place, although my leg muscles felt like I deserved first place. My legs were sore for six days after the race. My next 5k attempt was in 2015 at the age of 42 in my local hometown. I had no intention of placing at all. I ended up running worse than my first 5k by almost two minutes. I placed second with no training at all. I thought I would have learned a lesson by now - nope.

In May 2016, I was flying to Las Vegas for our yearly guys' trip. I was reading a *Sky Mall* magazine, and I came across an article called "Top 100 things to do in Las Vegas." Number eight on the list was run a race through the streets of Las Vegas. During the race, the city blocks off sections of the strip. I was hooked. They offered a 5k, 10k, half marathon and marathon. I liked walking a lot; in fact, one of my favorite things to do in Las Vegas was to see how many steps I could get in a day (my record to date is 42,000). The Rock-and-Roll Half Marathon/Marathon would be taking place in November 2016. I scoured the Internet for any information related to training for a half marathon.

My wife asked me, "Why in the world do you want to run a half marathon?" I told her because I was physically able to. She said, "You just want to put one of those 13.1 stickers on the back of your car." But truthfully the real reason was much deeper than that. Whenever I catch a fresh dump of powder on my snowboard, there is no other experience like it. I feel like a kid again, and I feel alive. The real reason I wanted to run was because I wanted to feel the accomplishment, feel the pain and feel the glory of crossing the finish line all the while feeling alive. Running allows me to unleash that competitive kid inside me who yearns to feel alive.

## *Help an Author Out*

Thanks for reading! If you've enjoyed this book, please leave me a short, gleaming review on Amazon. I take the time to read every review so that I can change and update this book based on reviewer feedback.

# http://geni.us/ZzGBs

If you've just finished your first half marathon race and you want someone to tell, send me an email. I would be delighted to hear from you.

**Follow me on Facebook and Twitter:**

Twitter: @BeginR2FinishR

Facebook: facebook.com/BeginnerToFinisher/

Website: www.halfmarathonforbeginners.com

Email: scottmorton@halfmarathonforbeginners.com

# Sign up for FREE EBook releases of my new books at: **http://geni.us/NRtsKu**

## Beginner to Finisher Series:

## **READ FOR FREE** with Kindle Unlimited.

### Available Now

*Why New Runners Fail: 26 Ultimate Tips You Should Know Before You Start Running! Book 1 of 5*

http://geni.us/WhyNewRunnersFail

*5K Fury: 10 Proven Steps to Get You to the Finish Line in 9 weeks or less! Book 2 of 5*

http://geni.us/5kFury

*Beginner's Guide to 10Ks: A Simple Step-By-Step Solution to Get You to the Finish line in 9 Weeks! Book 3 of 5*

http://geni.us/10KTitan

*Beginner's Guide to Half Marathons: A Simple Step-By-Step Solution to Get You to the Finish line in 12 Weeks! Book 4 of 5*

http://geni.us/HM4Beginners

### Coming Soon

*Long Run Motivation*

*Marathon Machine*

Made in the USA
Columbia, SC
19 July 2021